A FISHERMAN'S TALE

by Keith Faulkner and
Jonathan Lambert

Blackie Children's Books

Sam is fishing in a rock pool.
What is he going to find?

Sam's caught something! It's a tiny…

Sam puts the fish in a jar,

but when he gets home the fish has grown…

Sam moves the fish to a tank,

but the fish grows even...

Sam carries the fish to the bath,

but the fish grows still ...

bigger!

Sam wheels the fish back to the sea

and it grows and grows until...

'My goodness!' says Sam ...

Sam's new friend is a goldfish,